MOZART - Very Best
for piano

Catalog #07-2025

ISBN# 1-56922-048-4

Printed in the United States of America

Produced by John L. Haag

Exclusive Distributor for the Entire World:
CREATIVE CONCEPTS PUBLISHING CORP.
410 Bryant Circle, Box 848, Ojai, California 93024

MOZART - Very Best for piano

CONTENTS

ADAGIO 9

ADAGIO IN B MINOR 10

ALLEGRO 14

ARIA (From "Don Giovanni") 18

ARIA (From "The Marriage Of Figaro") 19

ARIETTA 37

CONCERTO NO. 21 (Theme) 20

EINE KLEINE NACHTMUSIK No. 1 Serenade
(A Little Night Music) 24

EINE KLEINE NACHTMUSIK No. 2 Romance
(A Little Night Music) 28

EINE KLEINE NACHTMUSIK No. 3 Menuetto
(A Little Night Music) 30

EINE KLEINE NACHTMUSIK No. 4 Rondo
(A Little Night Music) 32

FANTASIA IN C MINOR No. 1 38

FANTASIA IN D MINOR 48

GAVOTTE 52

GAVOTTE (From Ballet "Les Petits Riens") 54

GLOCKENSPIEL (From "The Magic Flute") 55

THE MAGIC FLUTE (Selected Themes) 56

MARCH FUNEBRE (Funeral March) 60

MINUET NO. 1 61

MINUET NO. 2 62

MINUET NO. 3 63

MINUET (From "Divertimento No. 1") 64

MINUET (From "Don Juan") 68

MINUET (From "Linz Symphony") 67

MINUET (From "Symphony in E Flat") 70

ROMANCE (From "The Piano Concerto In D Minor") 75

RONDO ALLEGRO 78

SONATA IN B FLAT 84

SONATA NO. 3 92

SONATINA 131

SONATINA No. 1 in C 94

SONATINA No. 2 in A 101

SONATINA No. 3 in D 108

SONATINA No. 4 in B Flat 112

SONATINA No. 5 in F 117

SONATINA No. 6 in C 122

THEME AND THREE VARIATIONS
  (From "Ah! Vous Dirai-Je Mamman") 132

TURKISH RONDO 136

TWO SHORT PIECES 142

TWO MINUETS 143

WALTZ IN A 138

WALTZ IN D 143

Circa 1774-1775

CAV. AMADEO WOLFGANGO MOZART ACCAD·FILARMON:DI BO
E DI VERONA

1777

Wolfgang Mozart and Joseph Hayden

1780

Medallion in red wax by L. Posch, 1788

Boxwood medallion by L. Posch, 1789

Circa 1786

The last authentic portrait of Mozart
April 17, 1789

Wolfgang Amadeus Mozart (1783)

Constance Mozart, his wife (1783)

1764-1765

Wolfgang Mozart's visit to Salomon Gessner at Zurich

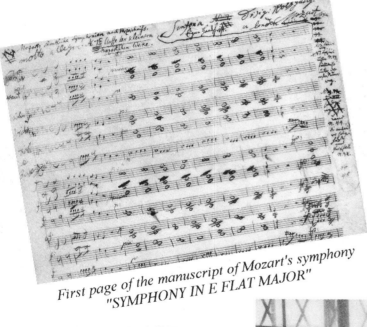

First page of the manuscript of Mozart's symphony
"SYMPHONY IN E FLAT MAJOR"

1778

1770

Room in which Mozart was born

1762

Painting on wax, 1778

Mozart at about thirteen years old

*The young master
at about 14 years of age*

*Leopold Mozart (his father)
playing with his son Wolfgang*

Miniature on ivory, 1777

1763

Wolfgang A. Mozart at his spinet, 1786

Reception of Mozart as a member of the "Philharmonic Academy of Bologna"

1785

Mozart's memorial statue in Salzburg

Mozart playing in the drawing room of the villa Bertamka

ADAGIO

Wolfgang Amadeus Mozart
(1756-1791)

ADAGIO IN B MINOR

Wolfgang Amadeus Mozart
(1756-1791)

ALLEGRO

Wolfgang Amadeus Mozart
(1756-1791)

ARIA (From "Don Giovanni")

Andantino

Wolfgang Amadeus Mozart
(1756-1791)

ARIA (From "The Marriage Of Figaro")

Wolfgang Amadeus Mozart
(1756-1791)

Marcato

CONCERTO NO. 21 (Theme)

Wolfgang Amadeus Mozart
(1756-1791)

EINE KLEINE NACHTMUSIK No. 1 Serenade
(A Little Night Music)

Wolfgang Amadeus Mozart
(1756-1791)

EINE KLEINE NACHTMUSIK No. 2 Romance
(A Little Night Music)

Wolfgang Amadeus Mozart
(1756-1791)

EINE KLEINE NACHTMUSIK No. 3 Menuetto

(A Little Night Music)

Wolfgang Amadeus Mozart
(1756-1791)

31

EINE KLEINE NACHTMUSIK No. 4 Rondo
(A Little Night Music)

Wolfgang Amadeus Mozart
(1756-1791)

ARIETTA

Wolfgang Amadeus Mozart
(1756-1791)

FANTASIA IN C MINOR No. 1

Wolfgang Amadeus Mozart
(1756-1791)

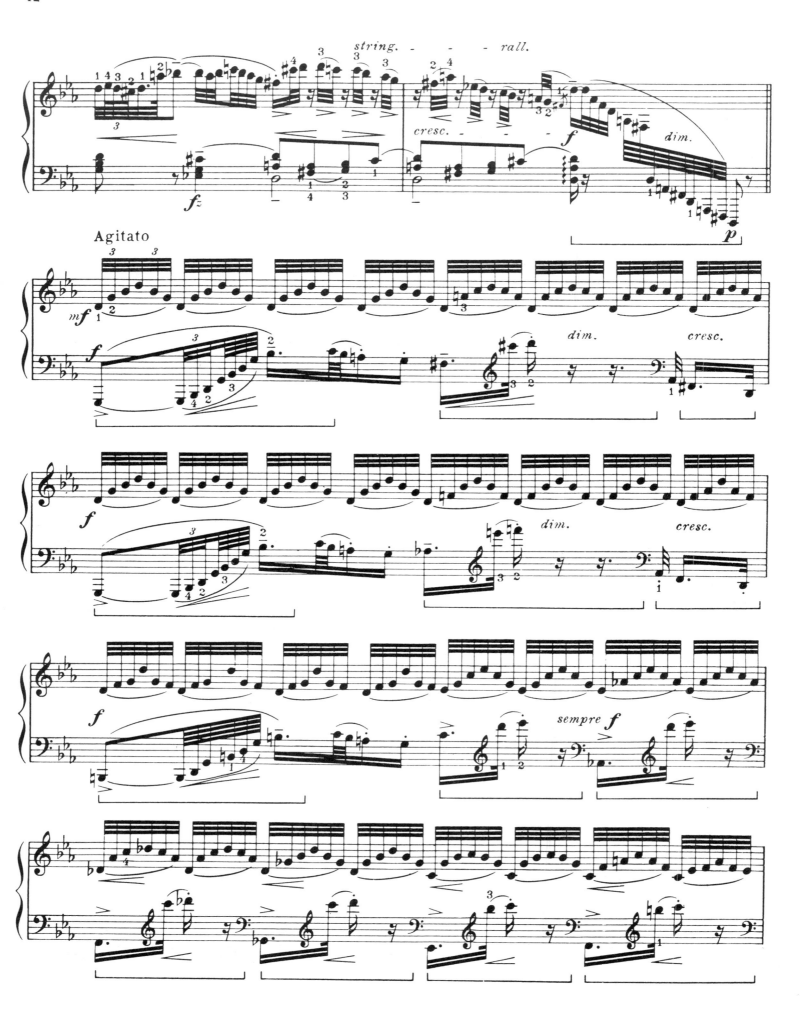

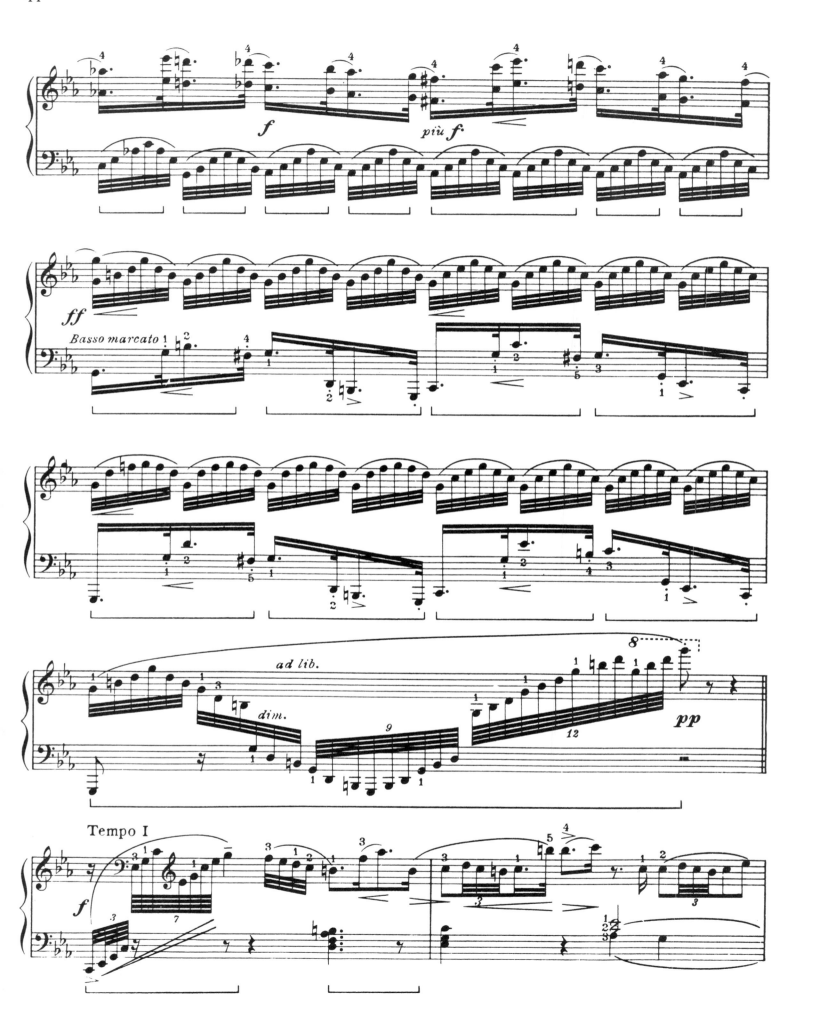

FANTASIA IN D MINOR

Wolfgang Amadeus Mozart
(1756-1791)

GAVOTTE

Wolfgang Amadeus Mozart
(1756-1791)

GAVOTTE (From Ballet "Les Petits Riens")

Wolfgang Amadeus Mozart
(1756-1791)

Moderato gracioso

GLOCKENSPIEL (From "The Magic Flute")

Wolfgang Amadeus Mozart
(1756-1791)

Allegro moderato

THE MAGIC FLUTE (Selected Themes)

Wolfgang Amadeus Mozart
(1756-1791)

Andantino (A Bird Charmer am I)

Andantino (Among Those Who Love.)

Allegro Moderato

MARCH FUNEBRE (Funeral March)

Wolfgang Amadeus Mozart
(1756-1791)

Adagio

MINUET NO. 1

Wolfgang Amadeus Mozart
(1756-1791)

MINUET NO. 2

Wolfgang Amadeus Mozart
(1756-1791)

MINUET NO. 3

Wolfgang Amadeus Mozart
(1756-1791)

Moderato.

MINUET (From "Divertimento No. 1")

Wolfgang Amadeus Mozart
(1756-1791)

TRIO

D.C. al Fine

MINUET (From "Linz Symphony")

Wolfgang Amadeus Mozart
(1756-1791)

MINUET (From "Don Juan")

Wolfgang Amadeus Mozart
(1756-1791)

MINUET (From "Symphony in E Flat")

ROMANCE
(From "The Piano Concerto In D Minor")

RONDO ALLEGRO

Wolfgang Amadeus Mozart
(1756-1791)

Allegro

SONATA IN B FLAT

Wolfgang Amadeus Mozart
(1756-1791)

SONATA NO. 3

Wolfgang Amadeus Mozart
(1756-1791)

SONATINA No. 1 in C

Allegro brillante

Wolfgang Amadeus Mozart
(1756-1791)

MENUETTO

Allegretto

TRIO

Menuetto da capo

SONATINA No. 2 in A

Wolfgang Amadeus Mozart
(1756-1791)

MENUETTO
Allegretto

TRIO

Menuetto da capo

Adagio

RONDO
Allegro

SONATINA No. 3 in D

Wolfgang Amadeus Mozart
(1756-1791)

MENUETTO
Allegretto

Fine

TRIO

Menuetto da capo

RONDO
Allegro

SONATINA No. 4 in B Flat

Wolfgang Amadeus Mozart
(1756-1791)

Andante grazioso

MENUETTO
Allegretto

Fine

TRIO

Menuetto da capo

RONDO
Allegro

SONATINA No. 5 in F

Wolfgang Amadeus Mozart
(1756-1791)

MENUETTO
Allegro

Menuetto da capo

POLONAISE

SONATINA No. 6 in C

Wolfgang Amadeus Mozart
(1756-1791)

MENUETTC
Allegretto

Fine

TRIO

Menuetto da capo

Adagio

FINALE
Allegro

SONATINA

Wolfgang Amadeus Mozart
(1756-1791)

Andante

THEME AND THREE VARIATIONS
(From "Ah! Vous Dirai-Je Mamman")

Wolfgang Amadeus Mozart
(1756-1791)

TURKISH RONDO

Wolfgang Amadeus Mozart
(1756-1791).

DS 𝄋 al Fine

WALTZ IN A

Allegretto.

Wolfgang Amadeus Mozart
(1756-1791)

WALTZ IN D

Wolfgang Amadeus Mozart
(1756-1791)

TWO SHORT PIECES

I.